07/16

AS Biology

There's a big jump from GCSE to AS Level Biology.
And with modules to take as early as January, you need to
make sure you hit the ground running.

This book will give you a Head Start — it covers all the AS basics
in enough detail to get you through the first few months, along with
practice questions to make sure you know all the facts.

It's ideal for use in the classroom, or for some extra study.
Make sure you get the grade you deserve.

What CGP is all about

Our sole aim here at CGP is to produce the highest quality
books — carefully written, immaculately presented and
dangerously close to being funny.

Then we work our socks off to get them out to you
— at the cheapest possible prices.

Contents

Section 7 — Transport in Plants

Section 8 — DNA and Mutation

Section 9 — Reproduction

Section 10 — Human Intervention

Section 11 — Survival Adaptations

Section 12 — Energy Flow in Ecosystems

Section 13 — Nutrient Cycles

Published by Coordination Group Publications Ltd.

Author:
Barbara Green

Design editors:
Chris Dennett
Becky May

ISBN: 978 1 84146 620 0
Groovy website: www.cgpbooks.co.uk
Jolly bits of clipart from CorelDRAW®
Printed by Elanders Hindson Ltd, Newcastle upon Tyne.

Plant and Animal Cells

What we see with a light microscope

Cells have different features so they can carry out different functions — but many features are common to all cells. A _light microscope_ can magnify up to 1500 times and allows us to see individual animal and plant cells and bacteria.

1) If the cells have been stained we can see the dark coloured nucleus surrounded by lighter coloured cytoplasm.
2) Tiny mitochondria and the black line of the cell membrane are also visible.
3) In plant cells the cell wall, chloroplasts and the vacuole can be seen.

4 things they both have in common:

3 Extras that only the plant cell has:

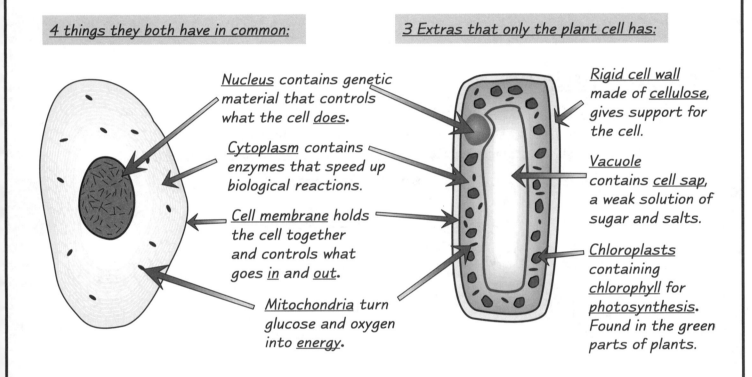

Nucleus contains genetic material that controls what the cell _does_.

Cytoplasm contains enzymes that speed up biological reactions.

Cell membrane holds the cell together and controls what goes _in_ and _out_.

Mitochondria turn glucose and oxygen into _energy_.

Rigid cell wall made of cellulose, gives support for the cell.

Vacuole contains cell sap, a weak solution of sugar and salts.

Chloroplasts containing chlorophyll for photosynthesis. Found in the green parts of plants.

Electron microscopes have a greater magnification

You may have thought that cytoplasm was pretty boring stuff but in fact it is packed full of tiny organelles (little organs) like mitochondria, ribosomes and endoplasmic reticulum.

1) Each type of organelle has a special function within the cell.
2) The detailed ultrastructure of cells was revealed in the 1950s when the electron microscope was invented.
3) An electron microscope can magnify objects up to 500 000 times and, more importantly, it allows greater detail to be seen. The image that is recorded is called an electron micrograph.

Function of Nucleus, Mitochondria and Cell Wall

Nucleus

1) The _nucleus_ is the control centre of the cell.
2) It contains _DNA_ (deoxyribonucleic acid), the coded information needed for cell division and for making proteins.
3) During cell division the chromosomes carrying the long DNA molecules coil up, becoming shorter and thicker and visible with a light microscope.
4) Electron micrographs show that there is a _double membrane_ around the nucleus.
5) Organisms made up of cells with a true nucleus are said to be _eukaryotic_ (pronounced like this: you-carry-ot-ick).
6) Organisms like bacteria, without a membrane around their DNA, are _prokaryotic_ (pro-carry-ot-ick).

Mitochondria

Mitochondria are about the size of bacteria, so they can be seen with a light microscope, but we need an electron microscope to see any of the detail.
Each mitochondrion has a _smooth outer membrane_ and a _folded inner membrane_:

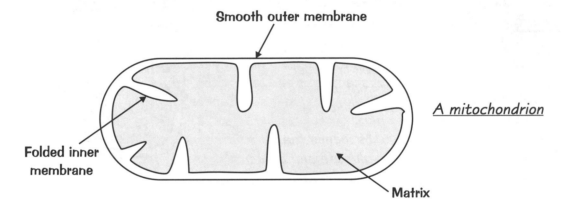

Smooth outer membrane

Folded inner membrane

Matrix

A mitochondrion

Aerobic respiration occurs inside the mitochondria.

Word equation: GLUCOSE + OXYGEN ➔ ENERGY + CARBON DIOXIDE + WATER

Their job is to capture the energy in glucose in a form that the cell can use. The energy ends up in molecules of _ATP_ (adenosine triphosphate). ATP is used in the cell to provide the energy for muscle contraction, active transport (called active uptake in some text books) and building large molecules from small ones, as well as many other processes.

Cell Wall

1) The _cell wall_ is relatively rigid and provides support for the plant cell.
2) It consists mainly of bundles of long, straight _cellulose molecules_.
3) Cellulose is a polymer of glucose — i.e. each molecule consists of many glucose molecules joined end to end.

Diffusion, Osmosis and Active Transport

Structure of the cell membrane

The _cell membrane_ is the very thin structure around an individual cell.
Don't confuse it with body membranes, which are made up from layers of whole cells.

1)   Electron micrographs show that the cell membrane consists of a double layer of _phospholipid_
     (pronounced: foss-foe-lip-id) molecules tightly packed together like the tiles of a mosaic.
2)   Bigger _protein molecules_ are embedded in the phospholipid molecules.
3)   Some proteins go all the way through the membrane and some only go halfway.

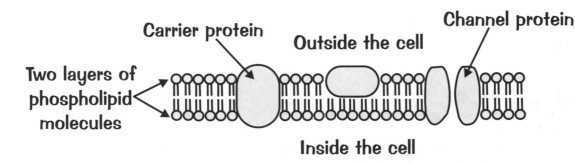

Do I really have to know this much detail?

1)   The answer is "Yes". Once you are familiar with the molecular
     structure of the membrane you can explain how the membrane
     controls the passage of substances in and out of the cell.
2)   Because the membrane only allows certain substances through
     it, it's described as being _partially permeable_.
3)   Substances pass through the membrane by 3 different
     methods: _diffusion_, _facilitated diffusion_ and _active transport_.

Diffusion

1)   The particles of liquids and gases are constantly moving about. This movement causes the
     particles to spread from an area of higher concentration to an area of lower concentration.
2)   Particles will diffuse through the cell membrane as long as they are small enough
     to pass through the very small gaps between the phospholipid molecules.
     Water, oxygen and carbon dioxide molecules can do this.
3)   The cell does not need to provide any energy for this process.

Osmosis

Osmosis is the diffusion of _water_ molecules across a partially permeable membrane
from a region of higher concentration of water molecules to a region of lower
concentration of water molecules. The cell does not need to provide energy.

Diffusion, Osmosis and Active Transport

Facilitated Diffusion

1) Glucose and many other water soluble molecules are too big to diffuse across the membrane by themselves. They must be helped across by <u>carrier proteins</u>.
2) Each substance has its own specific carrier protein.
3) For example, a molecule of glucose fits onto the outside end of a glucose carrier protein.
4) This causes the protein to change shape, allowing the glucose molecule to diffuse through it into the cytoplasm of the cell. The cell does not need to provide any energy.

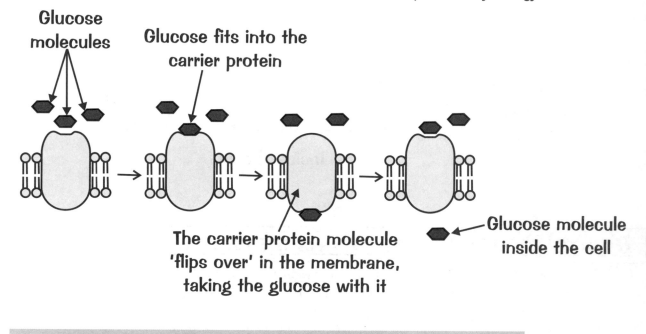

<u>Mineral ions</u> like sodium (Na⁺) and potassium (K⁺) have electrical charges on them, so they too need help to cross the membrane. Specific <u>channel proteins</u> in the membrane allow them to diffuse through.

Active Transport (or Active Uptake)

1) When a cell needs to move substances across the membrane from a region of low concentration to a region of higher concentration, it must provide <u>energy</u>.
2) The substance fits into a specific carrier protein, then molecules of ATP provide the energy to change the shape of the protein.
3) As it changes shape the protein actively transports the substance across the membrane.
4) These special carrier proteins are sometimes called "<u>pumps</u>" because they are moving substances against a concentration gradient.

Test Your Understanding

A lot of this section has been new to you. How much did you understand?

Have a go at these questions:

1) Name 3 things visible with a light microscope in both animal and plant cells.
2) Which type of microscope must be used to show the detail inside a cell?
3) What is an electron micrograph?
4) DNA is found in which organelle?
5) How could you distinguish a eukaryotic cell from a prokaryotic cell?
6) In which organelle does aerobic respiration occur?
7) Write the word equation for aerobic respiration.
8) The long, straight molecules of which substance provide strength in the cell wall of plant cells?
9) Name the two types of molecule that make up the cell membrane.
10) Name three ways substances can cross cell membranes.
11) What do we call the diffusion of water molecules through the cell membrane?
12) What is a partially permeable membrane?
13) What must the cell provide for active transport?
14) Which molecule, produced in mitochondria, is the immediate source of energy for cells?
15) Large numbers of which organelle would be present in a cell that actively transports a lot of glucose across its membrane? Explain your answer.

Answers

1) Any 3 from: nucleus, cell membrane, cytoplasm, mitochondria
2) An electron microscope
3) A record of the image produced by an electron microscope
4) The nucleus
5) Eukaryotic cells have a true nucleus. There is no membrane around the DNA of a prokaryotic cell.
6) The mitochondrion
7) glucose + oxygen → energy + carbon dioxide + water
8) Cellulose
9) Phospholipids and protein molecules
10) Diffusion, facilitated diffusion and active transport
11) Osmosis
12) A membrane through which only certain substances can pass.
13) Energy (or, ATP)
14) ATP (adenosine triphosphate)
15) You would expect to see large numbers of mitochondria because these would produce the ATP required for active transport.

Organs

Digestion

The human digestive system has three functions:
1) the <u>mechanical</u> breakdown of large pieces of food;
2) the <u>chemical</u> breakdown of large food molecules into smaller molecules;
3) the <u>absorption</u> of small food molecules into the bloodstream.

> Digestion is the chemical breakdown of large molecules into small molecules.

The chemical reactions involved in digestion are <u>hydrolysis reactions</u>.
The gut is simply a long, muscular tube that starts at the mouth and finishes at the anus:

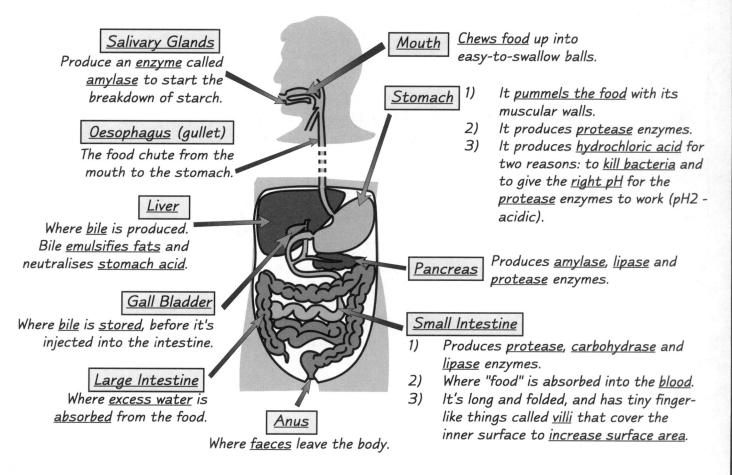

<u>Salivary Glands</u>
Produce an <u>enzyme</u> called <u>amylase</u> to start the breakdown of starch.

<u>Oesophagus</u> (gullet)
The food chute from the mouth to the stomach.

<u>Liver</u>
Where <u>bile</u> is produced. Bile <u>emulsifies fats</u> and neutralises <u>stomach acid</u>.

<u>Gall Bladder</u>
Where <u>bile</u> is <u>stored</u>, before it's injected into the intestine.

<u>Large Intestine</u>
Where <u>excess water</u> is <u>absorbed</u> from the food.

<u>Anus</u>
Where <u>faeces</u> leave the body.

<u>Mouth</u> <u>Chews food</u> up into easy-to-swallow balls.

<u>Stomach</u>
1) It <u>pummels the food</u> with its muscular walls.
2) It produces <u>protease</u> enzymes.
3) It produces <u>hydrochloric acid</u> for two reasons: to <u>kill bacteria</u> and to give the <u>right pH</u> for the <u>protease</u> enzymes to work (pH2 - acidic).

<u>Pancreas</u> Produces <u>amylase</u>, <u>lipase</u> and <u>protease</u> enzymes.

<u>Small Intestine</u>
1) Produces <u>protease</u>, <u>carbohydrase</u> and <u>lipase</u> enzymes.
2) Where "food" is absorbed into the <u>blood</u>.
3) It's long and folded, and has tiny finger-like things called <u>villi</u> that cover the inner surface to <u>increase surface area</u>.

The gut wall has three layers

1) The outer muscle layer pushes the food through the gut. This is called <u>peristalsis</u>.
2) The <u>submucosa</u> contains blood vessels.
3) The <u>mucosa</u> contains glandular tissue and is covered with a thin layer of <u>epithelial cells</u>.

In each region of the gut these layers have special features which allow that region to carry out a particular function.

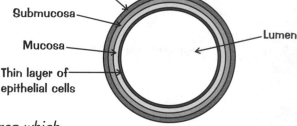

Muscle
Submucosa
Mucosa
Thin layer of epithelial cells
Lumen

The liver and pancreas are connected to the gut

Two glandular organs, the <u>liver</u> and the <u>pancreas</u>, produce fluids that flow into the small intestine through thin tubes called <u>ducts</u>.

Hydrochloric Acid and Bile

Hydrochloric acid is produced in the stomach

The wall of the stomach is thick and folded. In the deep pits between the folds, three different types of cell produce mucus, an enzyme and <u>hydrochloric acid</u> respectively.
The acid has two main functions:

1) It <u>kills microbes</u>.
2) It provides the <u>acidic conditions</u> necessary for the enzyme to work.

There are no enzymes in bile

The liver has many different jobs — producing <u>bile</u> is just one of them.

Bile is stored in the <u>gall bladder</u> until fatty food reaches the first part of the small intestine. This is the stimulus needed to make the gall bladder contract, forcing the bile along the <u>bile duct</u> and into the <u>duodenum</u> where it aids the digestion of fat.

1) It breaks down large fat droplets into many tiny droplets — a process called <u>emulsification</u>.
2) Emulsification is a physical process and is not the same as digestion, which is the chemical breakdown of molecules. (Many students confuse these two processes.)
3) The total surface area of the small droplets is greater than the surface area of the one large droplet of fat. More lipase enzyme molecules can now make contact with the fat and digestion is speeded up.

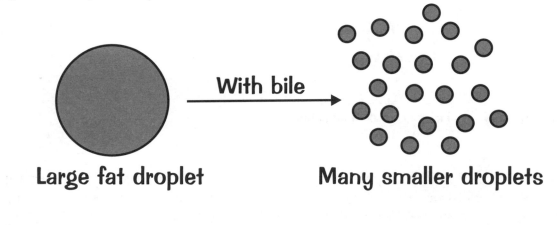

Large fat droplet   With bile   Many smaller droplets

Bile neutralises stomach acid

Bile also helps to provide the <u>alkaline conditions</u> necessary for the digestive enzymes of the small intestine.

Test Your Understanding

Test your memory by having a go at these questions:

1) What is digestion?

2) What type of chemical reaction is involved in digestion?

3) Food is moved through the gut by the rhythmical contraction and relaxation of the muscles of the gut wall. What is this action called?

4) Name the type of cell that lines the lumen of the gut.

5) Would sections of gut wall taken from the oesophagus, stomach and small intestine, look the same? Explain your answer.

6) Give two functions of hydrochloric acid in the stomach.

7) Does the liver produce digestive enzymes?

8) Describe the difference between the emulsification and the digestion of fat.

Answers

1) Digestion is the chemical breakdown of large food molecules into smaller molecules.
2) Hydrolysis reaction.
3) Peristalsis.
4) Epithelial cells.
5) No. You would expect the sections each region of the gut has adaptations that help it carry out a particular job.
6) Kills microbes and provides the right conditions for the enzyme to work.
7) No.
8) When fat is emulsified, large droplets are changed into many smaller droplets. The fat molecules inside the droplets are not changed in any way. When fat is digested the fat molecules are broken down into new substances.

Enzymes

Enzymes help to speed up biochemical reactions

In a living cell, thousands of biochemical reactions take place every second. The sum of these reactions is called _metabolism_. A single chain of biochemical reactions is called a _metabolic pathway_. Without enzymes, these reactions would take place slowly at normal body temperature.

1) Enzymes are _biological catalysts_.
2) They increase the rate of reactions.

How do enzymes act as catalysts?

1) Even reactions that release energy require an input of energy to get them going, e.g. the gas from a Bunsen burner doesn't burn until you provide heat energy from a match.
2) This input energy is called the _activation energy_. A reaction that needs a high activation energy can't start at a low temperature of 37 °C (i.e. body temperature)
3) Enzymes split a reaction into stages, each with a lower activation energy than the uncatalysed reaction. The cell can provide these small inputs of energy in the form of ATP.

This graph shows the activation energies of a reaction with and without an enzyme:

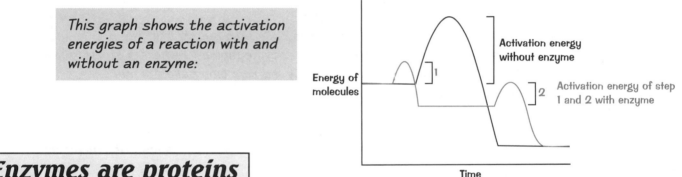

Enzymes are proteins

1) Proteins are chains of _amino acids_ attached to each other by strong _covalent bonds_.
2) Some proteins consist entirely of one type of amino acid but others can contain up to 20 different types.
3) The amino acids can be arranged in any sequence and proteins can be up to several hundred amino acids long.
4) The number of different proteins that are possible is almost unimaginable. Consider that there are several thousand ways of arranging a chain of just three amino acids, with each combination forming a different protein. Add one more amino acid to the chain and the number of possibilities leaps into the hundreds of thousands.

Answer the quick quiz below:

1) Where would you find a metabolic pathway: in a park, a cell, a field or alongside a main road? You may phone a friend or ask the audience.
2) Why are enzymes important?
3) What is activation energy?

Answers
1) In a cell.
2) They allow specific reactions to occur quickly at low temperatures.
3) Activation energy is the energy required to get a reaction started.

Enzymes

Each enzyme has its own special shape

1) The order in which the amino acids are arranged in a protein chain is called the <u>primary structure</u>.

2) Some chains coil up or fold into pleats that are held together by weak forces of chemical attraction called hydrogen bonds. The coils and pleats are the <u>secondary structure</u> of a protein.

3) Enzymes (and many other proteins) have a <u>tertiary structure</u>. The coiled chain of amino acids is folded into a ball that is held together by a mixture of weak chemical bonds (e.g. hydrogen bonds) and stronger bonds (e.g. sulphur bridges).

4) Enzymes are classed as <u>globular proteins</u> because of their roughly spherical shape.

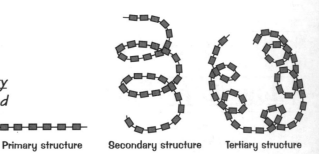

Primary structure   Secondary structure   Tertiary structure

Enzymes have an active site

1) A substance that is acted upon by an enzyme is called its <u>substrate</u>.

2) The <u>active site</u> is a region on the surface of the enzyme molecule where a substrate molecule can attach itself. It is where the catalysed reaction takes place.

3) The shape of the substrate molecule and the shape of the active site are <u>complementary</u>, i.e. they fit each other.

4) Almost as soon as the <u>enzyme-substrate complex</u> has formed, the products of the reaction are released and the enzyme is ready to accept another substrate molecule.

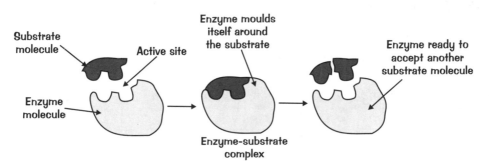

Substrate molecule   Active site   Enzyme moulds itself around the substrate   Enzyme ready to accept another substrate molecule

Enzyme molecule   Enzyme-substrate complex

Test your understanding with the questions below:

1) What is the primary structure of a protein?
2) Would a protease enzyme have the same primary structure as a lipase enzyme?
3) What type of bond holds together the secondary structure of an enzyme?
4) Look at the diagram above then describe the enzyme-substrate complex.

Answers

1) The order in which the amino acids are arranged in a chain.
2) No, the primary structure of every protein is different.
3) Weak forces of chemical attraction, called hydrogen bonds.
4) The substrate has attached to the active site of the enzyme and the enzyme has moulded itself around the substrate to make a perfect fit.

Enzymes

Enzymes are specific

1)   An enzyme usually catalyses one specific chemical reaction.
2)   The substrate molecule must be the correct shape to fit into the active site.
3)   Anything that changes the shape of the active site will affect how well the enzyme works.

The effect of temperature

As temperature increases, enzyme reactions become faster, because the molecules have more energy. However, at high temperatures the atoms of the enzyme molecule vibrate more rapidly and break the weak bonds that hold the tertiary structure together. The shape of the active site changes and the substrate can no longer fit in. The enzyme is said to be _denatured_.

The effect of pH

Acids and alkalis can denature enzymes. Hydrogen ions (H^+) in acids and hydroxyl ions (OH^-) in alkalis disrupt the weak bonds and change the shape of the active site.

Digestive enzymes

Most enzymes work inside the cell but the cells of the glandular tissue of the digestive system produce enzymes that are used outside the cell membrane. Digestion in humans takes place in the lumen of the gut and is said to be _extracellular_.

Glandular tissue	Enzyme produced	Substance digested	Products of digestion
Salivary gland	Amylase (carbohydrase)	Starch	Maltose (a sugar)
Gastric glands in stomach wall	Endopeptidase (protease)	Long protein molecules	Short protein molecules
Pancreas	Amylase Endopeptidases Lipase	Starch Short protein molecules Fats (lipids)	Maltose Very short protein molecules Fatty acids and glycerol
Cells in small intestine wall	Maltase (Carbohydrase) Exopeptidases	Maltose Very short protein molecules	Glucose Amino acids

See how much of that you've digested — answer the questions below:

1)   Explain why a denatured enzyme will not function.
2)   Why will amylase speed up the breakdown of starch but not cellulose?
3)   Name 4 regions of the digestive system that produce digestive enzymes.
4)   Which organ produces a carbohydrase, a protease and a lipase?

Answers

1)   The shape of the active site has changed and the substrate will no longer fit.
2)   A cellulose molecule is not the same shape as a starch molecule so it will be unable to fit into the active site on the amylase.
3)   Salivary glands, gastric glands in the wall of the stomach, pancreas and cells in the wall of the small intestine.
4)   The pancreas.

The Heart

Large animals need a circulatory system

1) Diffusion is only efficient over short distances, so any animal bigger than a simple worm needs a system that will bring glucose and oxygen into close contact with individual cells.

2) In humans, the heart pumps blood around the body through <u>blood vessels</u>. As it flows through the tissues, dissolved substances such as glucose, oxygen and carbon dioxide are exchanged between the blood and the cells.

The Cardiac Cycle

The <u>cardiac cycle</u> is the sequence of events that occurs during <u>one heartbeat</u>.

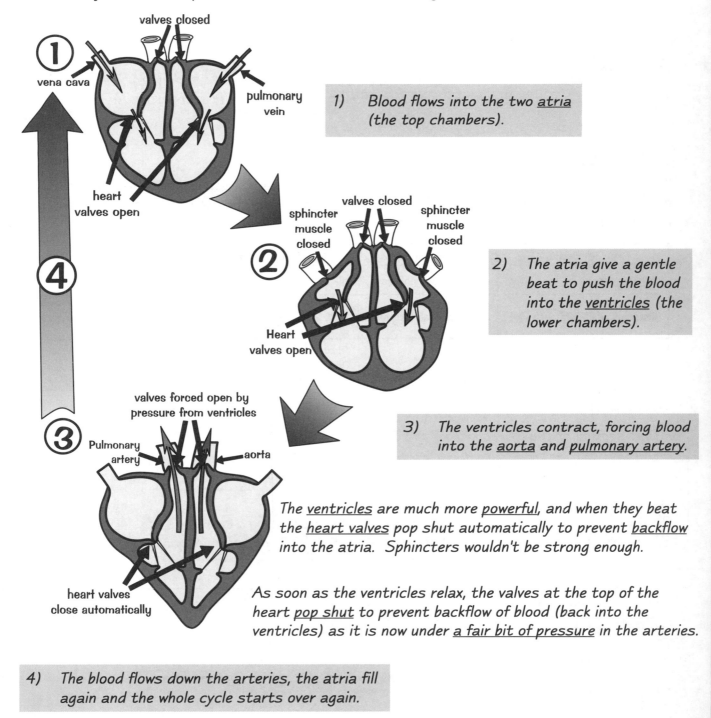

1) Blood flows into the two <u>atria</u> (the top chambers).

2) The atria give a gentle beat to push the blood into the <u>ventricles</u> (the lower chambers).

3) The ventricles contract, forcing blood into the <u>aorta</u> and <u>pulmonary artery</u>.

The <u>ventricles</u> are much more <u>powerful</u>, and when they beat the <u>heart valves</u> pop shut automatically to prevent <u>backflow</u> into the atria. Sphincters wouldn't be strong enough.

As soon as the ventricles relax, the valves at the top of the heart <u>pop shut</u> to prevent backflow of blood (back into the ventricles) as it is now under <u>a fair bit of pressure</u> in the arteries.

4) The blood flows down the arteries, the atria fill again and the whole cycle starts over again.

The Heart

Important facts to remember

1) The heart acts like two separate pumps. The right side sends blood to the lungs and the left side pumps blood around the rest of the body.
2) Blood always flows from a region of higher pressure to a region of lower pressure.
3) Valves in the heart prevent the blood from flowing backwards.
4) No energy is required to make the valves work — it's the blood pressing on the valves that makes them open and close.

The heart has its own pacemaker

1) Most muscles require nerve impulses from the central nervous system to make them contract.
2) The heart produces its own electrical impulses.
3) A group of specialised cells called the <u>sino-atrial node</u>, in the wall of the right atrium, sends out regular impulses.
4) These spread across the atria and down into the ventricles, making them contract.

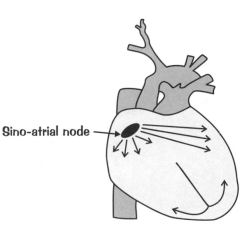

Sino-atrial node

The heart rate changes to suit the body's needs

1) The rate speeds up when we exercise and slows down when we rest or sleep.
2) 2 nerves link a region at the base of the brain (the <u>medulla</u>) to the sino-atrial node of the heart.
3) Nerve impulses from the <u>cardioacceleratory centre</u> in the medulla increase the heart rate.
4) Nerve impulses from the <u>cardioinhibitory centre</u> in the medulla decrease the heart rate.

Try these questions:

1) Explain why a fly maggot does not require a circulatory system.
2) Why is the wall of the left ventricle thicker than the wall of the right ventricle?
3) What is the function of the heart valves?
4) Do heart valves require energy to open and close?
5) The sino-atrial node is sometimes called the heart's natural pacemaker. What is its function?
6) In which region of the brain would you find the cardioacceleratory and cardioinhibitory centres?
7) What effect do impulses from the cardioinhibitory centre have on the heart rate?

Answers

1) The maggot is small enough for substances to reach all its cells by diffusion.
2) The right ventricle pumps blood only to the lungs but the left ventricle is a more powerful pump that sends blood to the rest of the body.
3) To keep the blood flowing one way.
4) No.
5) The sino-atrial node produces the regular electrical impulses that make the atria and ventricles contract.
6) In the medulla.
7) They decrease the heart rate.

Blood Vessels

Arteries, arterioles, capillaries, venules, veins

1)   <u>Arteries</u> carry blood away from the heart.
2)   They subdivide into smaller vessels called <u>arterioles</u>.
3)   Arterioles subdivide into microscopic vessels called <u>capillaries</u>.
4)   Capillaries join up to form <u>venules</u>, which join up to form <u>veins</u>.
5)   Veins return blood to the <u>heart</u>.

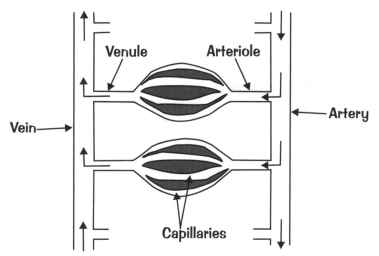

Arteries are elastic

Arteries have a thick wall compared to the diameter of
the lumen. There is an outer layer of <u>fibrous tissue</u>,
then a thick layer of <u>elastic tissue and smooth muscle</u>,
then a very thin inner layer of <u>endothelial tissue</u>.

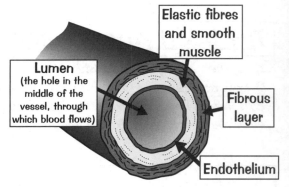

When the ventricles contract, blood enters the arteries at <u>high pressure</u>.
This stretches the elastic walls. When the ventricles relax, it is the elastic recoil of the
artery wall that keeps the blood pressure up. Important organs like the kidneys would not
be able to function if the blood pressure dropped too far between heartbeats.

Arterioles can contract

Arterioles are narrower than arteries and they have a higher proportion
of smooth muscle fibres and a lower proportion of elastic tissue.

When the circular muscle fibres of an arteriole
contract, the diameter of the lumen is reduced, so less
blood flows through that vessel. Arterioles can control
the amount of blood flowing to a particular organ.

Blood Vessels

Capillaries can only be seen with a microscope

Capillary walls consist of a single layer of endothelial cells.
Some capillaries have tiny gaps between the endothelial cells.

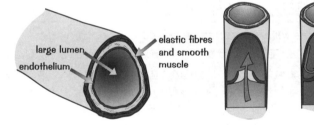

Capillary

Gaps between
endothelial cells

Capillaries are well suited to their job

1) The very thin walls and the gaps between the cells allow water and substances like glucose and oxygen to diffuse quickly from the blood into the cells. Waste products, such as carbon dioxide and urea, diffuse from the cells into the blood.
2) Organs contain thousands of capillaries, so altogether there is a _huge surface area_ for the exchange of substances.
3) Blood flows quite _slowly_ through capillaries. This allows more time for diffusion to occur.

Venules

Venules are about twice the diameter of capillaries
and have a thin layer of _fibrous tissue_ on the outside.

Veins have valves

A vein has a large lumen and a relatively thin wall containing some elastic tissue and smooth muscle. Veins also have _valves_ that prevent the blood flowing backwards.

large lumen

endothelium

elastic fibres
and smooth
muscle

When the _leg muscles_ contract they bulge and press on the walls of the veins, pushing the blood up the vein. When the muscles relax, the valves close. This action helps the blood return to the heart.

Have a go at these questions:

1) Explain the importance of the elastic tissue in the walls of arteries.
2) Describe how arterioles can control the amount of blood flowing to an organ.
3) Name three features of capillaries that maximise the exchange of substances between blood and cells.
4) Suggest why someone might faint if they stood absolutely still for a long time.

Answers

1) The elastic stretching and recoil of the artery walls prevents dramatic fluctuations in blood pressure that would damage important organs.
2) When the circular muscle fibres in the walls of arterioles contract they reduce the amount of blood flowing to the capillaries that they supply.
3) Very thin capillary walls. Many capillaries in each organ so there is a huge surface area. Blood flows relatively slowly through capillaries so there is more time for diffusion.
4) Leg muscles would not be contracting and relaxing so blood would not be helped back to the heart. Volume of blood in the heart would be less than usual and so the blood pressure in the arteries supplying the brain would decrease. This would result in insufficient oxygen and glucose reaching the brain cells.

Blood

The blood's main function is to <u>transport</u> materials to and from cells.

Haemoglobin has special properties

1) Red blood cells are packed with <u>haemoglobin</u>, a protein containing iron.
2) When there's a lot of oxygen present, one molecule of haemoglobin can combine with four molecules of oxygen to form oxyhaemoglobin — the haemoglobin is '<u>100% saturated</u>'.
3) When less oxygen is present, fewer molecules of oxygen combine and the haemoglobin is less than 100% saturated.

It would be reasonable to expect that a graph of '% saturation of haemoglobin' against 'concentration of oxygen' would be a straight line (i.e that the two would be proportional).

However, when experiments are carried out and the results plotted, the line of best fit is <u>S-shaped</u>:

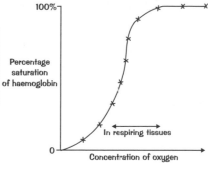

4) Haemoglobin has special properties that allow it to become fully saturated with oxygen in the capillaries around the <u>alveoli</u> of the lungs, where there is a <u>high concentration of oxygen</u>.
5) Then when it reaches respiring tissue, where there is less oxygen, it can give up almost all of its oxygen immediately — so the rate of respiration in the tissues isn't slowed down because of an oxygen shortage.

Carbon dioxide changes the properties of haemoglobin

1) Respiring tissues produce <u>carbon dioxide</u>.
2) If there's a lot of carbon dioxide present, the haemoglobin is <u>less efficient</u> at <u>taking up</u> oxygen (i.e. it needs to be exposed to a lot of oxygen before it becomes fully saturated).
3) But, when there's a lot of carbon dioxide present, the haemoglobin becomes <u>more efficient</u> at <u>releasing</u> oxygen (i.e. it can release more oxygen molecules in areas of fairly high oxygen demand).
4) This is good because it means that <u>rapidly respiring tissues</u>, e.g. contracting leg muscles and brain cells, get more oxygen.
5) This effect of carbon dioxide concentration on the oxygen-binding properties of haemoglobin is known as the <u>Bohr effect</u>.

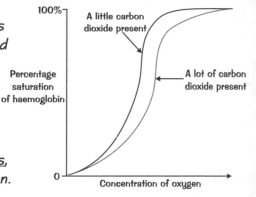

Understanding haemoglobin isn't easy — test yourself with these questions:

1) Name the substance picked up by the blood in the lungs.
2) Why is there a relatively low concentration of oxygen in liver tissue?
3) How many molecules of oxygen are bound to a haemoglobin molecule when it is fully saturated?
4) Which gas affects the oxygen-binding properties of haemoglobin?
5) Under what circumstances does a tissue require the most oxygen?

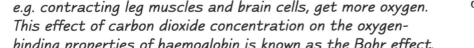

Answers
1) Oxygen
2) Respiration in the liver cells uses up oxygen.
3) 4
4) Carbon dioxide
5) When it is rapidly respiring.

Structure of the Thorax

Lungs have a very large gas exchange surface

Large active animals, like mammals, have evolved complex blood systems and lungs to provide a <u>large surface area</u> for the efficient diffusion of oxygen and carbon dioxide.

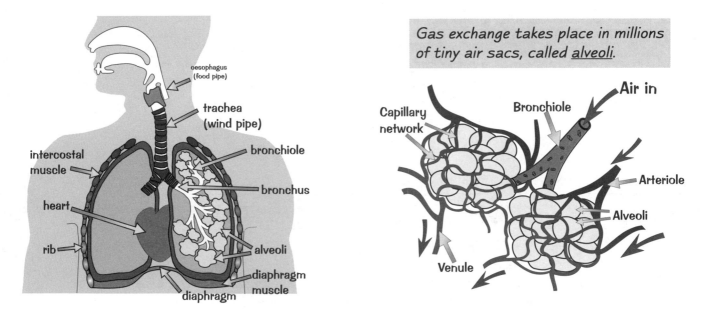

Gas exchange takes place in millions of tiny air sacs, called <u>alveoli</u>.

Alveoli have adaptations that increase the diffusion rate

1) The walls of the alveoli consist of a <u>single layer</u> of thin, flattened, epithelial cells. Diffusion happens faster when molecules only have to travel short distances.
2) Diffusion is faster when there is a bigger difference in concentrations between two regions. The blood flowing through the rich network of capillaries around the alveoli carries away the oxygen that has diffused through the alveolar walls. This ensures that there is always a <u>higher concentration of oxygen</u> inside the alveoli than in the blood. The reverse is true for carbon dioxide.
3) The alveolar walls are <u>fully permeable</u> to dissolved gases. Oxygen and carbon dioxide can pass easily through the cell membranes of the epithelial cells.

Water can cause problems in alveoli

1) The permeable membranes allow water to pass out of the epithelial cells. The thin layer of water that forms on the inner surface of the alveoli has <u>surface tension</u>.
2) This gives it the properties of an elastic membrane which can make it very difficult to inflate the lungs.
3) To overcome this problem the alveoli produce a <u>surfactant</u> which reduces surface tension.
4) Very premature babies are unable to produce this surfactant and could die from exhaustion and suffocation. Treatment with an artificial surfactant, in aerosol form, now helps them to survive.

18

Breathing In and Breathing Out

Vertebrate lungs evolved from outpockets of the gut.
Air must flow in and out by the same route. This is called <u>tidal ventilation</u>.

Why do we need to breathe?

Ventilation ensures that air with a <u>high concentration of oxygen</u> is taken into the lungs and air with a <u>high concentration of carbon dioxide</u> is removed from the lungs. This maintains high concentration gradients between air and blood, increasing the rate of diffusion of oxygen and carbon dioxide.

If volume increases, air pressure decreases

If the volume of an enclosed space is increased, the pressure inside it will decrease.
1)   The lungs are suspended in the <u>airtight thorax</u>.
2)   Increasing the volume of the thorax decreases the air pressure in the lungs to below atmospheric pressure. Air flows into the lungs, inflating them until the pressure in the alveoli equals that of the atmosphere.
3)   Decreasing the volume of the thorax increases the pressure in the lungs and air flows out until the pressure in the alveoli drops to atmospheric pressure.

<u>Breathing In...</u>

1)   <u>Intercostal muscles</u> and <u>diaphragm</u> <u>contract</u>.
2)   Thorax volume <u>increases</u>.
3)   This decreases the pressure, so air <u>flows in</u>.

<u>...and Breathing Out</u>

1)   <u>Intercostal muscles</u> and <u>diaphragm</u> <u>relax</u>.
2)   Thorax volume <u>decreases</u>.
3)   Air flows <u>out</u>.

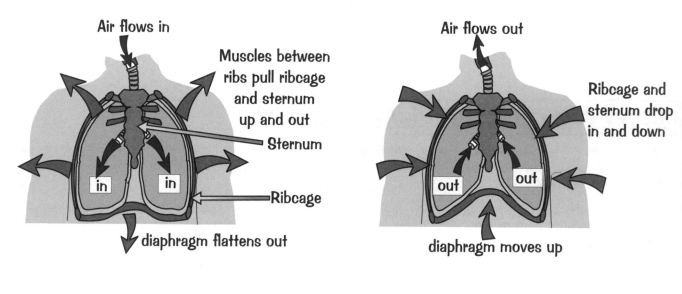

Air flows in — Muscles between ribs pull ribcage and sternum up and out — Sternum — in — in — Ribcage — diaphragm flattens out

Air flows out — Ribcage and sternum drop in and down — out — out — diaphragm moves up

Test Your Understanding

Take a deep breath and have a go at these:

1) In which part of the lungs does gas exchange take place?

2) Describe the shape of the cells that make up the walls of the alveoli and explain how their shape suits their function.

3) Name three substances that pass easily through the epithelial cell membranes.

4) What is a surfactant?

5) Describe the relationship between volume and pressure in an enclosed space.

6) Choose the correct word to complete the following sentence. Air always flows from a region of higher/lower pressure to a region of higher/lower pressure.

7) Which two sets of muscles contract when we breathe in?

8) Does breathing out require energy?

9) What are you eating when you tuck into barbecued spare ribs?

Answers

1) Alveoli
2) The epithelial cells are thin and flattened. The gases can diffuse quickly because the distance is small.
3) Oxygen, carbon dioxide and water.
4) A substance that reduces surface tension.
5) When the volume increases, the pressure decreases and when the volume decreases, the pressure increases.
6) Air always flows from a region of higher pressure to a region of lower pressure.
7) The intercostal muscles and the diaphragm muscles.
8) No.
9) You are eating a pig's intercostal muscles.

Aerobic Respiration in Mitochondria

Have another look at page 2 to remind yourself of the function of the <u>mitochondria</u>.

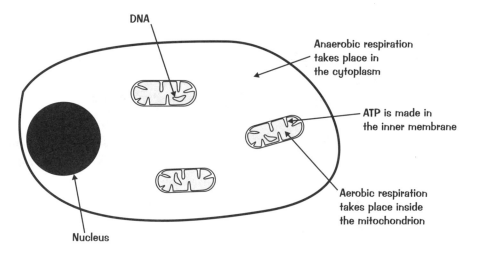

The ancestors of mitochondria may have been bacteria

1) There is a theory that millions of years ago the ancestors of mitochondria existed as aerobically respiring bacteria.

2) It has been suggested that the first eukaryotic animal cells evolved when these aerobic bacteria invaded anaerobic bacteria 1.5 billion years ago.

3) Anaerobic respiration in eukaryotic cells takes place in the cytoplasm and aerobic respiration only occurs in the mitochondria.

4) The discovery that mitochondria have their own DNA, which controls their division, supports this <u>Endosymbiotic</u> (pronounced: endo-sim-by-ot-ick) Theory of Eukaryotic Evolution.

Aerobic respiration involves oxygen

1) Each 6-carbon glucose molecule ($C_6H_{12}O_6$) is split into two <u>3-carbon pyruvate</u> (pie-roo-vate) molecules. The series of chemical reactions involved takes place in the cytoplasm and is called <u>glycolysis</u> (gly-kol-li-sis). A little energy is released during glycolysis.

2) The pyruvate passes into the centre of a mitochondrion (the matrix), where it is oxidised (when there is a good supply of oxygen). Carbon dioxide and water are released as waste products.

3) The large amount of energy released during oxidation is used to make many molecules of ATP in the folded, inner membrane of the mitochondrion. An inorganic phosphate group (P_i) is bonded to a molecule of <u>adenosine diphosphate</u> (ADP) to make each molecule of <u>adenosine triphosphate</u> (ATP).

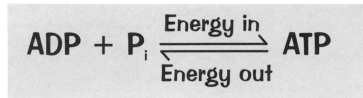

$$ADP + P_i \xrightleftharpoons[\text{Energy out}]{\text{Energy in}} ATP$$

Each ATP molecule can be used as a small package of energy within the cell.

Anaerobic Respiration and Lactic Acid

Anaerobic respiration does not require oxygen

Oxygen is in short supply in muscle cells during strenuous exercise.
This is when <u>anaerobic respiration</u> takes over.

1) The <u>pyruvate</u> that is produced by glycolysis is converted into <u>lactic acid</u>.
2) This process allows glycolysis to keep going, releasing some energy.

> GLUCOSE ➜ PYRUVATE + a little energy
> PYRUVATE ➜ LACTIC ACID

Unfortunately, nerve cells lack the enzyme that converts pyruvate to lactic
acid, so our brain cells are destroyed rapidly in the absence of oxygen.

Lactic acid dissociates into ions

Lactic acid dissociates into <u>hydrogen</u> ions (H^+) and <u>lactate</u> ions.

> LACTIC ACID ➜ H^+ + LACTATE$^-$

The hydrogen ions lower the pH in the muscle cells and this causes two main problems:

1) The enzymes involved in glycolysis don't work well in acid conditions.
   Glycolysis slows down.
2) The muscle proteins change shape and this interferes with muscle
   contraction. The muscles feel stiff and painful.

<u>Athletes</u> train to improve the blood circulation to their muscles so that the
hydrogen ions and the lactate are removed quickly. Training also increases the
amount of oxygen carried in the blood, so anaerobic respiration is less likely to occur.

What happens to the lactate?

The breathing rate remains high for some time after exercise has stopped.
Extra oxygen is required to remove the lactate. This is known as the <u>Oxygen Debt</u>.

First the lactate is converted back to pyruvate. Then two things can happen:

1) The pyruvate is oxidised, releasing energy
   to produce ATP. This process (<u>aerobic
   respiration</u>) occurs in the mitochondria and
   requires oxygen (see P. 20).
2) <u>Carbon dioxide</u> and <u>water</u> are produced as
   waste products.
3) Pyruvate is converted back into glucose,
   then glycogen, in the muscles and the liver.
   This process requires energy.

22

Test Your Understanding

Try answering these questions — see how much you know:

1) Which type of respiration takes place in mitochondria?
2) What is the Endosymbiotic Theory of Eukaryotic Evolution?
3) What evidence is there to support the theory?
4) In which part of the cell does glycolysis take place?
5) Is any energy released during glycolysis?
6) How many pyruvate molecules are produced from one glucose molecule?
7) Name the molecule that carries small amounts of energy to the different parts of a cell.
8) In which part of a cell does anaerobic respiration take place?
9) During anaerobic respiration, pyruvate is converted into lactic acid. Which energy-releasing process does this allow to continue?
10) Lactic acid dissociates into which two products?
11) Give two effects of an increased concentration of hydrogen ions in muscle cells.
12) When exercise stops, what happens to the lactate produced during anaerobic respiration?

Answers

1) Aerobic.
2) Eukaryotic cells may have originated when aerobic bacteria invaded anaerobic bacteria.
3) Mitochondria have their own DNA.
4) In the cytoplasm.
5) Yes, a little.
6) 2
7) Adenosine triphosphate (ATP)
8) In the cytoplasm.
9) Glycolysis.
10) Hydrogen ions and lactate ions.
11) Slows down glycolysis because the enzymes do not work well. Causes muscle stiffness and pain because muscle contraction is interfered with.
12) All of the lactate is converted back to pyruvate. Then some pyruvate is oxidised, in aerobic respiration, and the rest is changed back into glucose, then glycogen.

Section 5 — Respiration

Chloroplasts

Chloroplasts give leaves their green colour

Not all plant cells contain chloroplasts. Most roots are not green. It would be a waste of energy and materials for plants to produce chloroplasts for cells that don't receive light. Chloroplasts contain chlorophyll and are the site of photosynthesis — the process by which light energy is converted into chemical energy.

Chloroplasts are full of membranes

1) A chloroplast is surrounded by a double membrane. Unlike those of a mitochondrion, both membranes are unfolded.
2) Arising from the inner membrane is a series of internal membranes. These membranes consist of circular sacs called thylakoids (thile-ack-oids). Many chlorophyll molecules are embedded in the thylakoid membranes.
3) A stack of thylakoids is called a granum (grar-num). The plural of granum is grana.
4) The thylakoids of one granum may be connected to other grana.
5) The fluid in which the grana are suspended is called the stroma.
6) Like mitochondria, chloroplasts contain their own DNA.

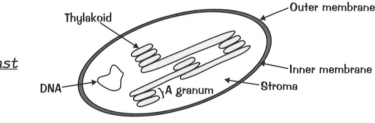

A chloroplast

Photosynthesis takes place in two stages

1) In the first stage of photosynthesis, chlorophyll molecules absorb light energy, which is transferred to protein molecules in the membranes to produce ATP.
2) The second stage takes place in the stroma. The ATP is used to convert carbon dioxide to carbohydrate.

Have a go at answering these:

1) Name the molecule that absorbs light energy.
2) How many membranes are around a chloroplast?
3) What are thylakoids?
4) In which part of a chloroplast is carbon dioxide converted to carbohydrate?

Answers
1) Chlorophyll.
2) 2
3) Flattened sacs of internal membranes that arise from the inner membrane surrounding the chloroplast.
4) In the stroma.

What Happens to the Glucose?

Plants use glucose for lots of different things

1) Some of the glucose produced by photosynthesis is used _immediately_ in _respiration_ to provide energy.
2) In a growing plant much of the glucose will be changed into _cellulose_ to build new _cell walls_.
3) _Proteins_ and different _sugars_ are all produced from glucose.
4) What's left is converted into _starch or oil_ and stored until it is required.
5) Building large molecules from small molecules like this requires energy.

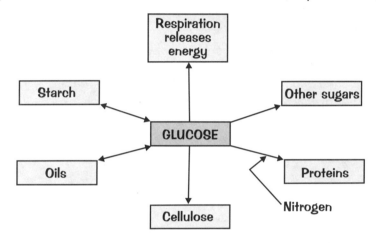

Carbohydrates contain three elements

Carbohydrates contain _carbon_, _hydrogen_ and _oxygen_.
Plants contain several types of carbohydrate; sugars, starch and cellulose.

1) Sugars are small, water-soluble molecules that taste sweet.
2) They are divided into two groups: _monosaccharides_ (mono-sack-a-rides) and _disaccharides_ (die-sack-a-rides).
3) Monosaccharides are the single units from which all the other carbohydrates are built. _Glucose_ and _fructose_ are both monosaccharides.

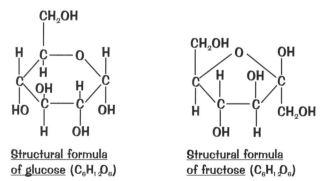

Structural formula of glucose ($C_6H_{12}O_6$)

Structural formula of fructose ($C_6H_{12}O_6$)

4) Disaccharides are formed when two monosaccharides are joined together by a chemical reaction. A molecule of _water_ is also formed.

GLUCOSE + GLUCOSE → MALTOSE (a disaccharide) + WATER
GLUCOSE + FRUCTOSE → SUCROSE (a disaccharide) + WATER

What Happens to the Glucose?

Starch is a polysaccharide

Polysaccharides are <u>polymers</u> of monosaccharides.
A starch molecule consists of a <u>long, coiled chain</u>
of glucose molecules. The insoluble, compact
molecules are an ideal way of <u>storing glucose</u>.

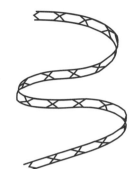

Starch molecule

Cellulose is a polysaccharide

Like starch, cellulose is a polymer of glucose, but the <u>bonding</u> between the glucose units
is different. As a result, the cellulose molecule is long and straight.
Several cellulose molecules can lie side by side to form <u>microfibrils</u>. The molecules are
held together by many weak <u>hydrogen bonds</u>. Microfibrils strengthen the cell wall.

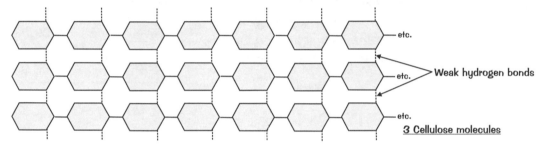

etc.

Weak hydrogen bonds

etc.

etc.

<u>3 Cellulose molecules</u>

Lipids contain carbon, hydrogen and oxygen

Lipids are <u>oils and fats</u>. Plant oils belong to a group of molecules called <u>triglycerides</u>.
A triglyceride consists of a molecule of <u>glycerol</u> with <u>three fatty acids</u> attached to it.

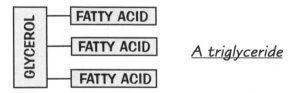

GLYCEROL	— FATTY ACID
	— FATTY ACID
	— FATTY ACID

<u>A triglyceride</u>

A fatty acid molecule is a long chain of carbon atoms with an acid group (-COOH) at the end.
Hydrogen atoms are attached to the carbon atoms. If every carbon atom in the chain is joined by
a single bond, we say that the fatty acid is <u>saturated</u>. If one or more of the bonds is a double
bond, it is said to be <u>unsaturated</u>. A fatty acid with many double bonds is <u>polyunsaturated</u>.

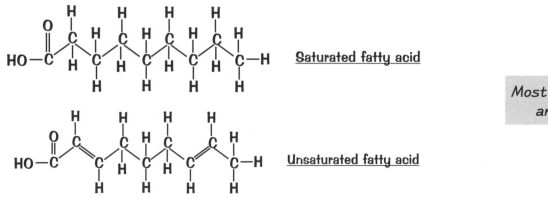

<u>Saturated fatty acid</u>

Most plant triglycerides
are unsaturated.

<u>Unsaturated fatty acid</u>

What Happens to the Glucose?

Proteins contain nitrogen

Before glucose can be converted into protein, plants must take in <u>nitrogen</u>, in the form of <u>nitrate</u>, from the soil. They also need <u>sulphur</u>, in the form of <u>sulphate</u>. Proteins all contain carbon, hydrogen, oxygen and nitrogen, and some contain sulphur. Proteins are composed of long chains of <u>amino acids</u>.

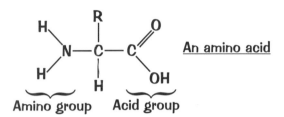

<u>An amino acid</u>

Amino group   Acid group

There are twenty different amino acids used in proteins. All have the same structure as the one in the diagram but R can be one of twenty different chemical groups. Here are four of them. Don't worry, you don't have to learn them.

Amino acid	R-group
Glycine	-H
Alanine	$-CH_3$
Serine	$-CH_2OH$
Cysteine	$-CH_2SH$

Test your understanding

See if you can answer these questions:

1) Do plants respire?
2) Do plants need energy to build large molecules from small molecules?
3) How do they get the energy?
4) Name two monosaccharides.
5) Which disaccharide is composed of two molecules of glucose?
6) Name two polysaccharides.
7) Why does a plant convert glucose into starch and oil?
8) Which element is always present in proteins but never in carbohydrates and lipids?

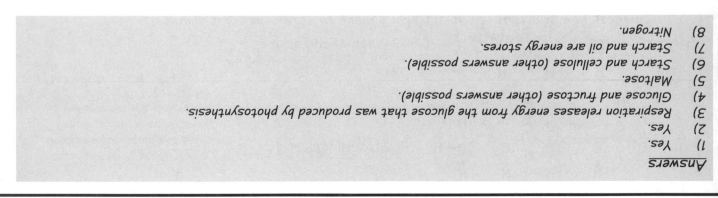

Answers
1) Yes.
2) Yes.
3) Respiration releases energy from the glucose that was produced by photosynthesis.
4) Glucose and fructose (other answers possible).
5) Maltose.
6) Starch and cellulose (other answers possible).
7) Starch and oil are energy stores.
8) Nitrogen.

Transpiration

Evaporation from the leaves and stems of plants is called _transpiration_. It has two main effects:

1) It _transports_ water and minerals.
2) It _cools_ the plant.

If the rate of transpiration is greater than the rate of water uptake by the roots, the plant wilts.

But, plants can't avoid transpiration, even if they need to — it happens because their leaves are exposed to the Sun during photosynthesis.

Plants have adaptations that reduce water loss

1) The _waxy cuticle_ that covers stems and leaves reduces water loss but it is impermeable to carbon dioxide.
2) _Stomata_ (singular — 'stoma') have evolved to solve this problem. Most plants only open their stomata when the light intensity is high enough for a good rate of photosynthesis.
3) They close them at night and can close them during the day if water loss is too great.

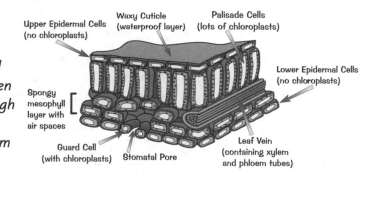

Upper Epidermal Cells (no chloroplasts)

Waxy Cuticle (waterproof layer)

Palisade Cells (lots of chloroplasts)

Lower Epidermal Cells (no chloroplasts)

Spongy mesophyll layer with air spaces

Guard Cell (with chloroplasts)

Stomatal Pore

Leaf Vein (containing xylem and phloem tubes)

Certain factors increase the rate of transpiration

Water molecules generally diffuse from a region of higher water concentration to a region of lower water concentration. The bigger the difference in concentration, the faster the movement.

1) Air inside a leaf is always saturated with water, so any decrease in _humidity_ outside the leaf will increase the rate of transpiration.
2) An increase in _temperature_ increases the evaporation rate of the water. It also increases the amount of water vapour that the air can contain. This maintains a concentration gradient.
3) When _wind speed_ increases, the water molecules are carried away from the area around the stomata and the concentration gradient increases.

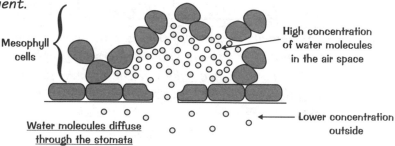

Mesophyll cells

High concentration of water molecules in the air space

Lower concentration outside

Water molecules diffuse through the stomata

Have a go at these questions:

1) What is transpiration?
2) Suggest how transpiration might help a plant to survive in a hot climate.
3) Why do plants need stomata?
4) Name three conditions that increase the rate of transpiration.

Xylem and Phloem Tissue

Xylem tissue transports water and minerals from roots

Water from the soil enters and travels through the root in two different ways:

The **symplast system**:
- Some water moves through **cytoplasm pathways** that continue from cell to cell, connecting adjacent cells — this means water doesn't have to cross any cell membranes.

The **apoplast system**:
- These are the **non-living parts** and include the cell walls and the spaces between the cells.
- Again, there are no membranes to regulate the passage of water and dissolved minerals.

Before water can enter either the symplast or the apoplast system, it must pass through the membranes of a layer of cells called the **endodermis**, through osmosis.

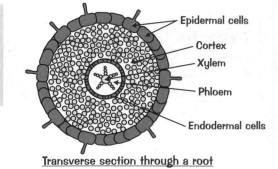

Transverse section through a root

Epidermal cells
Cortex
Xylem
Phloem
Endodermal cells

How does water reach the top of tall trees?

The cells that make up the tubes (vessels) of **xylem tissue** are dead, waterproof and hollow.

1) In **transpiration**, water evaporates from **mesophyll cells** inside the leaf leaving a higher concentration of solutes.
2) Water from the nearest xylem vessel enters the mesophyll cells by **osmosis**.
3) Water molecules stick together because of weak hydrogen bonds between them — this is called **cohesion**.

4) As water molecules leave the xylem vessel they pull up further molecules, so the whole column of water is pulled up.
5) Transpiration is pulling the water column upwards and gravity is pulling it down, so the water column is under **tension**.
6) The **adhesion** of water molecules to the sides of the xylem vessels stops the column breaking.

Phloem transports organic compounds

1) The movement of carbohydrates and other organic compounds in plants is known as **translocation**.
2) It occurs in the **sieve tubes** of the phloem tissue.
3) **Companion cells** next to the sieve tubes are believed to actively transport sugar into the sieve tubes, and then water follows by **osmosis**.

Sieve plate
Companion cell contains many mitochondria
Ordinary plant cells
Sieve tube
Vertical section of phloem tissue

Have a go at these questions:

1) Which part of the cell does water in the symplast system move through?
2) Would xylem be part of the symplast or the apoplast?
3) Why is the column of water in the xylem under tension?
4) Why do companion cells contain many mitochondria?

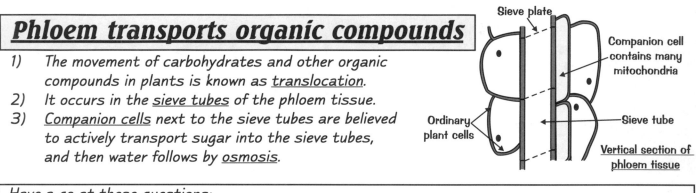

Answers
1) Cytoplasm.
2) Xylem cells are dead so they are apoplast.
3) Transpiration is pulling the water up and gravity is pulling it down.
4) For respiration to release energy for active transport of sugar.

The Code for Proteins

What causes different characteristics in organisms?

Different proteins are responsible for different characteristics.
Enzymes, hormones and antibodies are examples of proteins. They are
all made up of chains of <u>amino acids</u>. It is the order of the amino acids
in a protein that determines its structure, and hence how it works.

<u>Protein A</u>

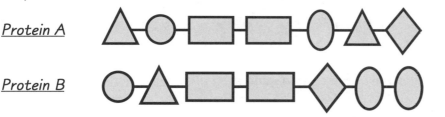

(N.B. Each different shape
represents a different
type of amino acid.)

<u>Protein B</u>

How does a cell know which type of protein to produce?

The <u>genes</u> on the chromosomes are responsible for the types of protein produced.
Genes are sets of coded instructions for building proteins. One gene codes for one protein.

How does the code work?

Unravel a chromosome and you have a very long molecule called DNA (<u>deoxyribonucleic acid</u>).
The DNA molecule is shaped like a twisted ladder, with each "rung" made from two chemicals
called bases. There are four different bases; <u>A, T, C and G</u>:

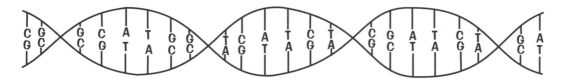

A gene is a short section of DNA. The sequence of the bases
in that section of the DNA controls the order in which the
amino acids are put together in a particular protein.

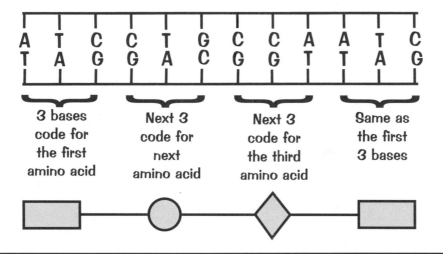

| A T C | C T G | C C A | A T C |
| T A G | G A C | G G T | T A G |

3 bases code for the first amino acid   Next 3 code for next amino acid   Next 3 code for the third amino acid   Same as the first 3 bases

Mutation

Changing the code

If the order of the bases in the gene is changed then the sequence of the amino acids in the protein will be changed. The protein will have a different shape and that may affect the way it works.

People with cystic fibrosis have a gene with three bases missing. Remember, three bases code for one amino acid, so the protein that is produced has one amino acid missing. The abnormal protein can't function properly and, as a result, the mucus in the lungs and digestive system is very thick and sticky.

Changes in the sequence or in the number of bases in a gene are called mutations. They occur naturally and, although most are harmful, some are neutral in their effect. In rare cases, a mutation can be responsible for a characteristic that is beneficial and increases the chances of survival of an organism and any offspring which inherit the mutant gene.

Increasing the rate of mutation

Ionising radiation (including X-rays, ultraviolet light and alpha, beta and gamma radiation from radioactive materials) and certain chemicals can damage or destroy DNA molecules. They are called mutagens. The greater the exposure to a mutagen, the greater the chance of mutation.

Test your understanding

Have a go at these questions:

1) Are enzymes fats, proteins or carbohydrates?
2) What is a gene?
3) Suggest why scientists refer to the genetic code as a triplet code.
4) What is a mutation?
5) What is a mutagen?

Answers
1) Proteins
2) A gene is a section of DNA that codes for a particular protein.
3) It is called a triplet code because three bases make up the code for one amino acid.
4) A mutation is a change in a gene. It occurs when the order of the bases becomes altered for some reason.
5) A mutagen is a substance or type of radiation that can damage DNA.

Section 8 — DNA and Mutation

Asexual and Sexual Reproduction

Asexual reproduction involves only one parent

1) In _asexual reproduction_ a single organism produces offspring by dividing into two organisms or by splitting off a piece of itself.
2) All the offspring are genetically identical.
3) The cells divide by _mitosis_ (like most cells).

> Bacteria and many plants reproduce asexually.

In mitosis the DNA copies itself then the cell divides once

1) Before the cell starts to divide, every DNA molecule must replicate. The two new molecules remain attached to each other in a small region called the _centromere_.
2) Each DNA molecule becomes supercoiled and compact. Each chromosome can now be seen with a light microscope and appears as two _chromatids_ lying side by side, joined by the centromere.

3) The nuclear membrane breaks down and the chromosomes line up along the _equator_ (middle) of the cell:
4) The centromeres split and the chromatids separate and are dragged to opposite ends of the cell:

5) A _nuclear membrane_ forms around each set of chromatids (exact copies of the original chromosomes) and the _cytoplasm divides_:

Sexual reproduction involves two sex cells

1) In _sexual reproduction_, the offspring are genetically different from their parents and from each other. This produces variation in a population.
2) Each parent produces sex cells (_gametes_) containing just one set of genetic material. This involves a special kind of cell division, called _meiosis,_ and the gametes are described as being _haploid_.
3) During fertilisation the nuclei of the gametes join together to form a _zygote_. The zygote has two complete sets of genetic material, and is said to be _diploid_.
4) The zygote grows by simple cell division (mitosis) to form the _embryo_.

In meiosis, DNA copies itself then the cell divides twice

1) Human body cells each contain 46 chromosomes, which can be sorted into 23 pairs of similar size and shape (_homologous pairs_). One of each pair came from the male parent and one from the female parent.
2) Special cells in the testes and ovaries undergo meiosis to produce _gametes_.
3) The DNA _replicates_, so each of the 46 chromosomes becomes two chromatids joined by a centromere.
4) The 46 chromosomes sort themselves into the _23 homologous pairs_, then they separate. One of each pair goes to one side of the cell and one goes to the other.
5) The cytoplasm now divides. Each of the new cells contains 23 chromosomes (consisting of two chromatids joined by a centromere).
6) In both of these new cells the chromatids separate and the cytoplasm divides to form two cells.
7) At the end of meiosis, _four haploid cells_ have been produced from every original diploid cell.

Cloning and Selective Breeding

Farmers do not want variation in their crop

Growers select a variety of plants with good qualities, e.g. flavour, size and disease resistance, and they reproduce them *asexually*. Each plant is a *clone*, so the whole crop has the same qualities.

Methods of *vegetative propagation* include:

1) Planting *tubers* (e.g. whole potatoes) to produce new plants.
2) Taking *cuttings* and planting them in moist soil.
3) *Grafting a cutting* onto the lower part of an existing plant. Most fruit trees are produced this way.
4) *Micropropagation* in a laboratory. This modern technique involves growing small plantlets from tiny pieces of plant tissue on sterile growing media. When the plantlets have developed shoots and roots they are planted in ordinary soil. Thousands of new, disease-free clones can be produced this way.

Now mammals can be cloned artificially

1) Eggs and sperm are collected from animals with the desired characteristics. The eggs are fertilised in the laboratory.
2) The fertilised eggs (*zygotes*) are allowed to grow into small embryos of about 16 cells.
3) The 16 cells are separated from each other and encouraged to grow by themselves. These cells are allowed to grow into 16 embryos.
4) The embryos are implanted into 16 *surrogate mothers*. The young animals produced this way are clones and are genetically identical to each other but differ from their parents.

Dolly the sheep was very special

1) Although mature body cells contain all the genes necessary to produce a new organism, it was believed that once they had become specialised to carry out a particular function they could not be made to divide like a fertilised egg.
2) However, in 1997 scientists took the nucleus from an udder cell of a six-year-old sheep and inserted it into an egg cell, from which the nucleus had been removed.
3) They implanted the egg in a surrogate sheep and eventually a *lamb called Dolly* was born.
4) Dolly was a *genetically identical clone* of the sheep that had provided the udder cell nucleus.
5) Dolly was born healthy and went on to produce a lamb of her own as a result of normal mating.
6) In 2003 Dolly was put down because she had developed a progressive lung infection.

Cloning and Selective Breeding

Humans and selective breeding go back a long way

Humans have been selectively breeding plants and animals for thousands of years.

1) New varieties of plants and animals are produced by <u>sexual reproduction</u>.
2) Most of our crops and domestic animals are the result of selective breeding.
3) Male and female organisms with desirable characteristics are chosen as parents.
   This increases the chance that the offspring will have the same desirable characteristics.
4) Many of the offspring will not have the ideal combination of parental genes, so it may take
   many generations before the "perfect" organism is produced.
5) Humans do not always consider the <u>welfare</u> of the animals when breeding them.
   Many <u>pedigree dogs</u> suffer from problems that are rarely seen in <u>mongrels</u>.

Test your understanding

Find out how you're doing — answer these questions:

1) What is a clone?
2) List 4 methods of vegetative propagation.
3) Suggest a disadvantage of growing a field of potato plants that are genetically identical.
4) Describe how 16 identical piglets could be produced from a sow and a boar.
5) Describe how a piglet identical to a mature pig could be produced.
6) Suggest some desirable characteristics that a breeder might look for in potential parent pigs.

Genetic Engineering

Genetic engineering uses recombinant DNA technology

Recombinant DNA technology brings together techniques from the fields of _microbiology_ and _genetics_. This new branch of biology is often referred to as _Genetic Engineering_. Recombinant DNA is DNA that is made up of connected segments from different sources.

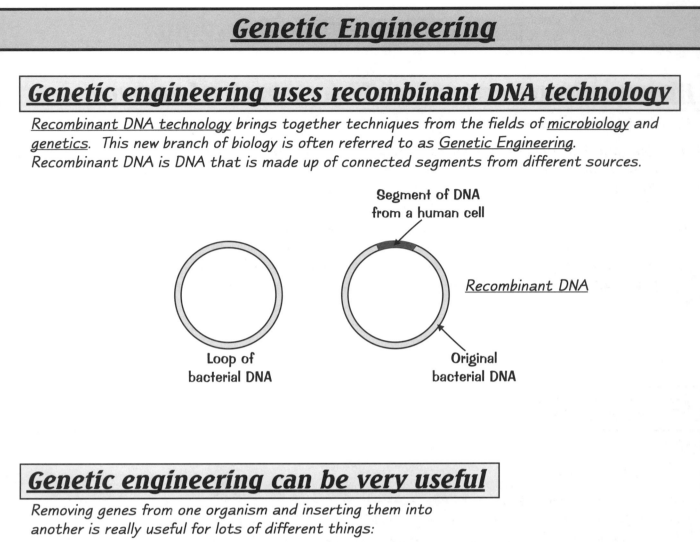

Segment of DNA
from a human cell

Recombinant DNA

Loop of
bacterial DNA

Original
bacterial DNA

Genetic engineering can be very useful

Removing genes from one organism and inserting them into another is really useful for lots of different things:

1) Genes that improve the keeping quality of fruit have been added to _tomato plants_.
2) Genes that improve _disease resistance_ have been added to cereal plants.
3) Genes that code for hormones, enzymes and antibiotics have been transferred into micro-organisms which then produce large quantities of these substances. _Insulin_ is produced this way for people with _diabetes_.
4) The fertilised eggs of cows and sheep have had human genes injected into them. Every cell of the animals that developed contained the human gene. The milk from these animals contains the protein coded for by the human gene. The gene can be passed on to their offspring. _Human alpha-1-antitrypsin_, which is used to treat the lung disease, _emphysema_, is produced by this method.

The DNA is first chopped into segments by enzymes

1) Even bacteria have enemies. Tiny viruses called _bacteriophages_ attack and inject their genetic material into the bacteria. Some bacteria protect themselves by producing enzymes that cut up the DNA into non-infectious fragments. The enzymes are called _restriction endonucleases_.
2) Scientists have been able to isolate these enzymes from bacteria.
3) There are hundreds of different restriction endonucleases. Each one will only cut the DNA molecule where it recognises a specific base sequence. Choosing the correct enzyme means that individual genes can be removed.

Genetic Engineering

We use vectors to get the DNA fragment into a bacterium

1) Plasmids can be used as vectors.
2) Plasmids are small circular molecules of DNA that occur naturally in some bacteria. They replicate themselves and don't interfere with the bacterium's own DNA.

3) Isolated plasmids are cut open with the same restriction endonuclease that was used to cut out the gene. The open plasmids are then mixed with the gene.
4) An enzyme called ligase is added. This joins the gene into the plasmid.

Shock treatment makes the bacteria accept the plasmids

1) Bacteria are kept in cold calcium chloride solution for 30 minutes. This makes the cell membrane more permeable.
2) Recombinant plasmids are added and the mixture is warmed. This allows some of the plasmids to get through the bacterial cell membrane.
3) Bacteria containing the recombinant plasmids are identified and cultured (grown) in industrial fermenters.
4) The gene in the plasmid produces the protein, which can then be extracted.

Test your understanding

Lots of new words. How many can you remember?

1) What is recombinant DNA?
2) Name a hormone that is produced by bacteria containing a human gene.
3) What is a restriction endonuclease?
4) What is a plasmid?
5) What does ligase do?

Answers
1) DNA that is made up of connected segments of DNA from different sources.
2) Insulin
3) An enzyme that cuts the DNA molecule at a specific place.
4) A small circular molecule of DNA that occurs naturally in some bacteria. It replicates itself and does not interfere with the bacterium's own DNA.
5) It is an enzyme that joins together two pieces of DNA.

Section 10 — Human Intervention

Size and the Surface Area to Volume Ratio

Small objects have relatively large surface areas

1)   Have you ever wondered why there are no large single-celled organisms or
     why big animals are made up of millions of tiny cells instead of a few large ones?

2)   The main reason relates to the changes in the _surface area to
     volume ratio_ of an object as it increases in size.

3)   Look at the 3 cubes in the diagram below. The smallest cube has the biggest surface
     area to volume ratio and the biggest cube has the smallest surface area to volume ratio.

Surface area 6 cm²
Volume 1 cm³
Surface area : Volume
          6 : 1

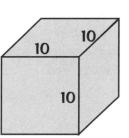

Surface area 600 cm²
Volume 1000 cm³
Surface area : Volume
         0.6 : 1

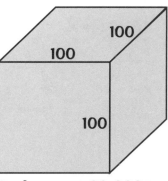

Surface area 60,000 cm²
Volume 1,000,000 cm³
Surface area : Volume
        0.06 : 1

Surface area is important for exchange

Cells or organisms need to exchange materials and heat with their environment.
More chemical reactions will be able to occur every second in a cell with a large
volume than in one with a small volume. Therefore oxygen, nutrients, waste
products and heat need to be exchanged across the membrane at a faster rate.
With increasing volume this becomes an _ever-increasing problem_.

Maintaining a constant body temperature can be tricky

Multicellular organisms with specialised cells and structures have solved this problem.

1)   _Respiration_ in mammals produces lots of _heat_, so they need to stop themselves overheating.

2)   Mammals have adaptations which allow them to maintain a _constant body temperature_.

3)   A large mammal has a small surface area to volume ratio. A small mammal, such as a mouse,
     has a large surface area to volume ratio.

4)   In a hot climate the mouse has the advantage and can lose heat quicker than a large elephant.
     To overcome the problem, elephants have evolved _huge, moveable ears_ which increase the
     animal's surface area. The ears have a good blood supply and by flapping them backwards and
     forwards the elephant can dissipate a great deal of heat.

5)   In a cold environment small mammals are at a disadvantage, because they lose heat too
     quickly, so they must _eat constantly_ or curl up and _hibernate_ to stay alive.

Size and the Surface Area to Volume Ratio

Test your understanding

See if you can answer the questions below:

1) Which has the bigger surface area to volume ratio, a small organism or a large organism?

2) Which process produces a lot of heat in mammalian cells?

3) In the Arctic which animal will find it easier to keep warm — an adult male polar bear or an adult male arctic fox? Explain your answer.

Answers

1) A small organism
2) Respiration
3) The polar bear. It is larger than the fox so it has a smaller surface area to volume ratio than the fox. The bear's rate of heat loss will be less than that of the fox.

Reducing the Rate of Transpiration

Plants with special adaptations to dry environments are called <u>xerophytes</u> (zee-row-fites).

Some plants only open their stomata at night

1) During the night these plants must obtain all the <u>carbon dioxide</u> they will need for photosynthesis the following day.

2) If the plant simply relied on the carbon dioxide that could diffuse into the intercellular spaces of the leaf it would only reach the same low concentration as is in air. This would be enough for only a few minutes of photosynthesis. Instead, the mesophyll cells combine the carbon dioxide with an organic acid to form <u>malic acid</u>. They do this as fast as the carbon dioxide comes in, increasing the diffusion gradient and allowing more carbon dioxide to diffuse into the leaf.

3) During the day, while the stomata are closed, the malic acid is broken down to release carbon dioxide for photosynthesis.

4) Plants that can do this are said to have <u>crassulacean acid metabolism</u> (CAM).

Many desert plants have no leaves

1) Photosynthesis takes place in the <u>stems</u>.
2) Spines and tiny hairs trap water molecules in the air next to the stomata, reducing the rate of transpiration.
3) Water is stored in some stems.
4) The <u>spines discourage animals</u> from eating the succulent stems.
5) The epidermal cells of cacti have a thick, waterproof layer of <u>wax</u> on the outside.

Marram grass can survive on sand dunes

1) The stomata on the underside of the leaf are in sunken pits. Hairs around the pits <u>trap moist air</u>.

2) When conditions are very dry the grass rolls its leaves into <u>cylinders</u> with the stomata on the inside. Moist air trapped inside the cylinder prevents transpiration.

Thick waterproof cuticle

Moist air trapped inside

Stomata in sunken pits

Try answering these questions:

1) What is a xerophyte?
2) Give an advantage and a disadvantage of closing stomata through the day.
3) Which gas is stored as malic acid in plants with crassulacean acid metabolism (CAM)?
4) How can a dense covering of hairs on the undersides of the leaves help a plant survive in a dry environment?

Answers

1) A plant with adaptations which help it survive in dry conditions.
2) Advantage: Transpiration does not occur during the hottest part of the day so water is conserved.
   Disadvantage: Carbon dioxide cannot enter the plant for photosynthesis.
3) Carbon dioxide
4) Most stomata are on the underside of the leaf. The hairs trap moist air around the stomata so the water diffusion gradient is reduced and transpiration slows down. This helps the plant conserve water.

Pyramids of Numbers and Biomass

Each stage in a food chain is a trophic (feeding) level

1) The first level is occupied by the <u>producers</u>, the second by the <u>primary consumers</u>, the third by the <u>secondary consumers</u> and so on.
2) The producers are mainly green plants, algae and cyanobacteria. All of these produce their own food by photosynthesis. <u>Chemosynthetic bacteria</u> which obtain energy from inorganic compounds are also classed as producers.
3) Primary consumers are <u>herbivores</u> and secondary consumers are <u>carnivores</u>.

Ecological pyramids can show numbers or biomass

1) Ecological pyramids show relationships between organisms in different trophic levels.
2) One of the problems with pyramids of number is that they are often not pyramid shaped. A small cabbage plant is given the same status as a huge oak tree and every tiny parasite on a consumer is counted.
3) <u>Pyramids of biomass</u> help to overcome this. The total dry mass of organisms at each trophic level is estimated and compared.
4) The rectangles represent the <u>mass</u> of organisms per unit area or volume (e.g. grams per square metre or grams per cubic metre).

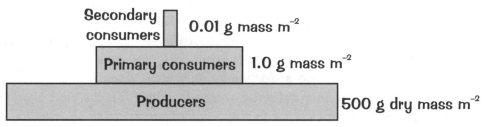

Secondary consumers — 0.01 g mass m^{-2}
Primary consumers — 1.0 g mass m^{-2}
Producers — 500 g dry mass m^{-2}

Pyramids of biomass have their faults

The biomass at a given moment in time is known as the <u>standing biomass</u>. This is what is sampled and it does not indicate the rate of production of biomass (the productivity). This can be misleading.

1) If the organisms at one level are being eaten as fast as they are being produced, the standing biomass might be small even though a large amount of biomass is passing to the next level every year. A fertile, grazed field would have a smaller standing biomass than an equivalent infertile field that is not grazed.
2) <u>Aquatic communities</u> can have <u>inverted</u> pyramids of biomass. This happens because <u>phytoplankton</u> are small but have such a high rate of cell division that a small standing biomass can feed a much larger biomass of herbivores that grow and reproduce much more slowly.

Zooplankton — 12 g m^{-3}
Phytoplankton — 4 g m^{-3}

(Phytoplankton is minute plant life and zooplankton is minute animal life, both found in water.)

Pyramids of Energy

Pyramids of energy are the most useful pyramids to use

1) In pyramids of energy the rate of production of biomass is taken into account. Each bar represents the <u>amount of energy per unit area</u>, or volume, that flows through the trophic level in a given period of time.

2) Examples of units that are used: kilojoules per square metre per year ($kJ\ m^{-2}\ yr^{-1}$) and kilojoules per cubic metre per year ($kJ\ m^{-3}\ yr^{-1}$).

3) Energy is lost (mainly as heat) at each level, so pyramids of energy are always pyramid shaped and never inverted.

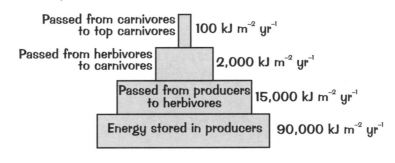

Passed from carnivores to top carnivores — $100\ kJ\ m^{-2}\ yr^{-1}$

Passed from herbivores to carnivores — $2{,}000\ kJ\ m^{-2}\ yr^{-1}$

Passed from producers to herbivores — $15{,}000\ kJ\ m^{-2}\ yr^{-1}$

Energy stored in producers — $90{,}000\ kJ\ m^{-2}\ yr^{-1}$

The efficiency of energy transfer between levels is low

1) Energy enters ecosystems mainly through photosynthesis, but only a small percentage of solar radiation that falls on producers ends up in the producers' tissues. Much of the glucose produced in photosynthesis is used in plant respiration.

2) Herbivores can't digest all of the material in producers, so some energy is lost in faeces. A lot of food digested and absorbed by animals is used for respiration, so only a little is converted into animal tissue and is available for the next trophic level.

3) Mammals and birds must maintain a constant body temperature so they have a high rate of respiration and lose a lot of energy as heat to the environment.

4) Dead producers and consumers and the faeces from consumers are food for bacteria and fungi. Microbes respire and energy is lost as heat to the environment.

Try answering these questions:

1) To which trophic level do the cyanobacteria belong?
2) Why are they placed in that level?
3) In a pyramid of biomass, what do the rectangles represent?
4) What type of community can have an inverted pyramid of biomass?
5) Are pyramids of energy ever inverted?
6) What is the main source of energy in most ecosystems?
7) In what form is most energy lost from an ecosystem?

Answers
1) Producers.
2) They produce their own food by photosynthesis.
3) The mass (strictly the dry mass) of organisms per unit area or volume at a particular feeding level and time.
4) An aquatic community.
5) No.
6) Solar energy which enters producers by photosynthesis.
7) Heat.

The Carbon Cycle

Bacteria and fungi are decomposers

Living organisms need large quantities of carbon, hydrogen, oxygen, nitrogen, phosphorus and sulphur, among other things. These elements are constantly being <u>recycled</u>.
Many of the <u>carbon</u> and <u>nitrogen</u> atoms in living organisms today are the same ones that were in the tissues of the <u>dinosaurs</u> and first mammals over 200 million years ago.

<u>Bacteria and fungi</u> play an important role in the recycling of carbon and nitrogen.

1) <u>Complex organic molecules</u> (molecules based on carbon) in dead organisms and faeces are broken down by micro-organisms. This is <u>decomposition</u>.

2) Bacteria and fungi do this by releasing digestive enzymes onto the organic material and then absorbing the products of digestion.
This method of feeding is called <u>saprophytic nutrition</u>.

The carbon cycle involves many different processes

1) Carbon in carbon dioxide enters plants by <u>photosynthesis</u>.
2) Some of the carbon stays in the carbohydrates, proteins and lipids in plant tissues, but some is released back into the atmosphere when carbon dioxide is produced during <u>respiration</u>.
3) Carbon passes into animals when they eat the plant tissues.
4) Some of the carbon stays in the animals' tissues but a lot is released during respiration. Carbon passes along the food chain.
5) Dead plants and animals and the faeces from living animals are eaten by the <u>decomposers</u>. Some carbon is used by the microbes for growth and some is released as carbon dioxide. When those microbes die others eat them.
6) Most decomposers require oxygen. If there is no oxygen available for respiration organic material does not decompose and the carbon remains locked up. Over millions of years, the plant and animal remains change into <u>fossil fuels</u> such as coal, oil and gas. The carbon is released as carbon dioxide when the fuels <u>burn</u>.
7) <u>Clearing and burning forests</u> also releases carbon dioxide into the atmosphere.

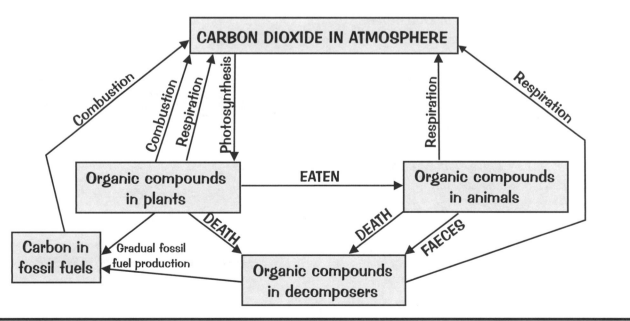

The Nitrogen Cycle

Proteins and nucleic acids contain nitrogen

Nitrogen gas makes up about 78% of the atmosphere, but most organisms cannot use nitrogen in its gaseous form. Only a few _nitrogen-fixing bacteria_ can convert the gas into biologically useful forms, so nitrogen is often in short supply in ecosystems.

1)   Most plants obtain their nitrogen by absorbing _nitrate ions_ (NO_3^-) from the soil.
2)   Proteins in dead animals, plants and faeces, and urea in urine are converted to nitrate ions in stages by different types of fungi and bacteria.
3)   _Decomposers_ digest proteins into amino acids.
4)   Amino acids and urea are _deaminated_ to form _ammonium compounds_. This is done by bacteria and the process is called _ammonification_.
5)   The ammonium ions (NH_4^+) are _oxidised_ to nitrite ions (NO_2^-) by one type of _nitrifying bacteria_.
6)   The nitrite ions are oxidised to _nitrate ions_ (NO_3^-) by another type of nitrifying bacteria.

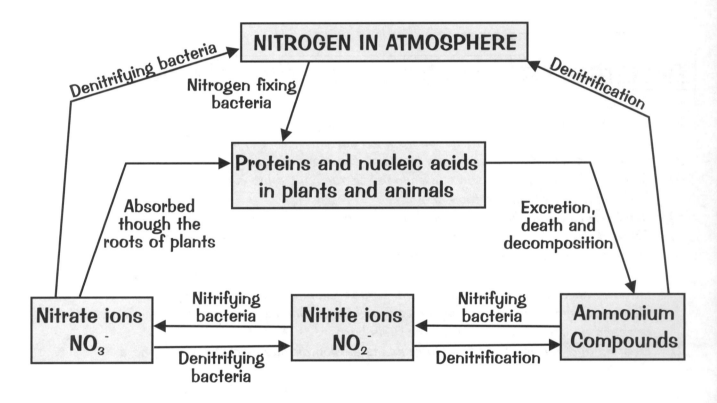

Not many plants can grow well in waterlogged soil

Nitrifying bacteria require _oxygen_ to form nitrate ions. Little oxygen is present in very wet ground. This is bad enough but it gets worse — there are some bacteria, called _denitrifying bacteria_, that use the oxygen in nitrate and nitrite ions when they respire releasing nitrogen gas into the atmosphere.

Page 43

Test Your Understanding

One last set of questions to have a go at:

1) Which types of micro-organisms are decomposers?
2) What is an organic molecule?
3) Are carbohydrates, proteins and lipids (fats) organic molecules?
4) How does carbon enter plants?
5) In what form is carbon released into the atmosphere during respiration and combustion?
6) Do decomposers respire?
7) How long does it take for fossil fuels to form?
8) Many of the carbon atoms in the carbon dioxide released when we burn fossil fuels are the same atoms that were in the Earth's atmosphere approximately 400 million years ago. True or false?
9) Nitrogen is an essential component of which two types of organic molecules?
10) Plants absorb nitrogen from the soil in what form?
11) Proteins in dead matter are digested into amino acids by what?
12) What are nitrifying bacteria?
13) What are denitrifying bacteria?

Answers

1) Fungi and bacteria.
2) A molecule based on carbon.
3) Yes.
4) As carbon dioxide used in photosynthesis.
5) Carbon dioxide.
6) Yes.
7) Millions of years.
8) True.
9) Proteins and nucleic acids.
10) Nitrate ions.
11) Enzymes produced by decomposers.
12) Soil bacteria that oxidise ammonium ions to nitrite and nitrate ions.
13) Soil bacteria that obtain oxygen by converting nitrite and nitrate ions into nitrogen gas in the atmosphere.

Section 13 — Nutrient Cycles

Index